The Day My Daddy Died

Written and Illustrated by Rebecca Mason
Cover concept by Elliot Mason

This book is dedicated with love to my three wonderful boys;
Elliot, Andrew, and Shane.
"My three sons" as their Dad used to call them.
May they always feel the light and love of their Dad,
and use that spark to light up the world.

Once upon a time,

There was the sweetest boy ever.

He was smart, curious, and loved to learn new things.

He spent his time riding bikes, building with Legos, and playing outside with his friends.

He lived with his family who he loved very much.

His life was happy, ordinary, and good.

But one regular day something happened
that would change this boy's life forever.
He didn't expect it, he wasn't ready for it,
and he didn't want it to be true when he heard it.
But despite not asking for it, it happened just the same.

He came home one day
like he had done a hundred times before.
But somehow on that day,
he sensed something different in the air.
He felt like the world as he knew it
was about to change, and his life
would never be the same again.

His Mom met him at the door and said that they
needed to talk.
The boy's heart beat a little faster
as they sat down in the living room.
She told him something bad had happened to his Dad.
The boy's heart pinched.
Somehow he knew what she was going to tell him,
but he didn't want to hear it.

He didn't want it to be true.

She told the boy that his Dad had gotten hurt.
She said sometimes people get a small hurt
and they can get better.
But other times people get a hurt so big that
they cannot get better, no matter how hard they try.
This is what had happened to his Dad.
He had gotten a very big hurt and he was not
going to get better, no matter how hard he tried.

This was the day his Daddy died.

The little boy sat in disbelief
as tears rolled down his cheeks.
His body grew so heavy
it felt like he would fall to the ground.
His Dad was gone.
All he could think of was that his Dad was gone.

He felt numb as his Mom's words began to sink in.
They felt heavy, and painful, and were too much to bear.
He wanted to jump out of his skin so he could escape
the pain he was starting to feel.
He knew it would take him to a place he did not want to go.

A wall of sadness crashed into him
like a big wave at the beach.
He felt like it would knock him over...

he felt like it was too much.

The boy couldn't believe his Dad was gone.

He was so young, so full of energy, and was so much fun!

He made everything an adventure.

He always told great stories and lit up the room with his laugh.

Just that morning his Dad had given him a big hug
and kiss before school.

How could all of that light have gone out?

The boy's heart pinched so much it hurt.
He felt like he would do anything in the world
to have his Dad back and make his dying not true.
He wanted to feel his Dad's hug and smell his smell.
He wanted to see the twinkle in his eyes
when he told his funny stories.
He wanted to hear his silly laugh again.
But most of all,
he wanted to tell his Dad how much he loved him.

The little boy kept watching their front door,
hoping his Dad would come home again.
He wanted him to walk through the door,
sweep the boy up in his arms, tell him
he was still here and that he loved him.
But his Dad never came back home.

The boy's Mom promised him he would be okay.
She said his sadness might feel like it comes in waves.
And when those sad waves crash into him, she would hold
him until they got smaller and didn't hurt as much.
She was here for him and would take care of him.
They would get through this together.

Missing his Dad was a pain that wouldn't go away.
It felt like everything inside the boy stopped.
And he thought the rest of the world
should just stop, too.
He didn't understand why everything around him
was still working when his whole world
had been turned upside down.

In time, the boy went back to school,
even though he didn't want to.
He did all the things he was supposed to do,
but he didn't care about them anymore.
It felt like he was just going through the motions.
His heart wasn't in it anymore.
His heart still missed his Dad.

Their house was a lot quieter now.
There was a big empty hole where his Dad used to be
and it was hard to get used to.
Friends and family came to visit but it still didn't fill up
the hole that his Dad dying had left.

After a while, the boy became angry.

When he saw his friends playing at the park
with their dads, he felt angry that his Dad
wasn't there to play with him.
He was jealous that his friends still
had their dads, and he didn't have his.
It seemed like everywhere he looked,
all he saw were other boys and girls with their dads.
And it all felt so unfair.

His Mom reminded the boy
that his Dad was still with him,
just in a different way now.
They would just have to listen harder to hear him
and look harder to see the good things
he would send their way.

The boy spent a long time crying and feeling mad.
But in time, he slowly began to heal.
He was sad sometimes, but not all the time.
He still cried, but not as often or as much.
And every time he cried he felt just a little bit better,
as if his tears were washing away the pain.

He felt relieved because his Mom told him
he would see his Dad again.
She said someday they would all be together again and he would
be able to hug his Dad and tell him how much he loved him.
And the little boy believed this with all of his heart.

The boy knew his Dad was still with him.
He could feel that part of him was still there.
And he knew his Dad could still hear him,
so he talked to him every day...

...because he knew his Dad was listening.

The little boy never stopped loving or missing his Dad,
but he began finding ways to hold on
to his good memories without feeling all of the pain.
He looked at pictures, watched family movies,
and talked about their adventures.
It helped him remember how much his Dad loved him,
and how much fun they had together.
He began to feel lucky that he had such a special Dad,
even though he only had him for a short time.

These thoughts and memories gave him
an inner strength that made him
feel as strong as a Superhero.
He felt like he could do anything
with his Dad inside his heart...

So he did.

He learned how to be happy again.
He remembered how to laugh
and play with his friends.
He started to care about school and having fun again.
He began to see the good
in things around him
and not take anyone for granted.
He realized how much of a gift life is.

And in time, that little boy followed his dreams
while holding his Dad in his heart.
He knew his Dad loved him,
was watching over him,
and was proud of him.

And that was the spark
that lit the boy's soul.

The Beginning.

Acknowledgements~

From the bottom of my heart, I'd like to thank my family, friends, and all of the wonderful people I've met along the way who have encouraged me to pursue the publishing of this book. After writing it so many years ago, I finally feel ready to share it with the world. I hope it is found and kindly received by those who find it helpful.

A special thanks to my dear friend Corinne Power, who by sheer determination was the gentle force behind the creation of this book. She encouraged me to keep going and see this project to completion. She was my art director, editor, overall cheerleader, and I am forever grateful. A special thanks to Lindsay Duggar for sharing her thoughts on illustrations. A heartfelt thank you to my Graphic Designing Aunt, Chris Geimer, who oversaw the technology aspects, answered my many questions, and kindly applied her expertise to the visual aspect of this book. Thank you to Tricia Brick for the writing the beautiful back cover and seeing merit in this project from the beginning, and to my sweet friend Jane Hunt for encouraging me to play with art again. Gratitude to my kiddos for their patience and support while I worked on this and all my friends and family who encouraged me in this endeavor. I'm not sure I could have crossed the finish line without the support from all of you.

Much Love, Rebecca

Author's Note~

I wrote this book shortly after my husband passed away in 2007. His death was sudden and tragic, and it shattered my family's safe world in an instant. I searched for children's books that would speak to how my boys were feeling. I wanted to find something that would directly relate to them and help them process the feelings of this unique kind of grief. But my searches left more to be desired. As I laid awake one sleepless night, I looked at my three small children snuggled in close to me sleeping soundly in my bed. I was determined to do my best for them and give them the support they needed in order to help them process this in the healthiest way possible. It was out of this deep desire that I began to write this story. I wanted them to know they were not alone in having their Daddy die. Because it felt like they were. When I read the finished story to them, they were surprised that another little boy out there knew exactly how they felt. And they said it made them feel better....so, we read it often.

It is my deepest desire that this story will also comfort your child or children in some way. I hope they can see themselves in it as my own children did. I hope that you and your children can find strength in the fact that you are unified with many in this experience; you are not alone, and you will get through this horrible time. And I hope that you will ultimately be triumphant in your grief journey and find the will and grace to move forward with love.

Light and Love,, Rebecca

In loving memory of Todd Eliot Mason
The Best Daddy ever

Made in the USA
Middletown, DE
04 March 2021